The Frontiers of SPACE

Mc Graw Hill **Wright Group**

The **McGraw-Hill** Companies

www.WrightGroup.com

 **Wright Group**

Copyright © 2011 by The McGraw-Hill Companies, Inc.

Printed in USA.

Send all inquiries to:
Wright Group/McGraw-Hill
P.O. Box 812960
Chicago, IL 60681

ISBN 978-0-07656411-8
MHID 0-07-656411-8

4 5 6 7 8 9 DOC 16 15 14 13 12 11

Contents

Theme Question 4

Selection 1
Biography
**Nicolaus Copernicus:
Changing the Universe** 6

    Think Back 28
    Think Ahead 29

Selection 2
Informational Text
Oh My Stars! 30

    Think Back 54
    Think Ahead 55

Selection 3
Realistic Fiction
The Brain and the Movie 56

    Think Back 78
    Think Ahead 79

Selection 4
Science Fiction
The New Kids 80

    Think Back 103

Respond to the Theme Question 104

    Glossary 106
    Index 110

Digital 21

Why do people study space?

Have you ever looked into the night sky and wondered about it? What are the stars made of? Where did they come from? Over the centuries, people have come up with many ideas about the night sky. Some of these ideas are being changed as scientists learn more.

Focus Questions

Selection **1**

What patterns and cycles do we find in space?

Selection **2**

How did people of the past explain objects in the night sky?

Selection **3**

How do people view space today?

Selection **4**

How might space be a part of our future?

 Preview

What patterns and cycles do we find in space? Preview pages 6–27. Then read *Nicolaus Copernicus: Changing the Universe* to find out.

Nicolaus Copernicus
CHANGING THE UNIVERSE

by MEISH GOLDISH

Chapter One
Early Years

Nicolaus Copernicus was born in Toruń, Poland, around 4:30 in the afternoon on February 19, 1473. It is odd that we know the time of his birth. Such details usually were not recorded back in the fifteenth century. So why do we know this fact about Copernicus?

During Copernicus's life, an **astrologer** drew a chart called a horoscope for him. A horoscope shows the positions of the stars and planets at the time a person is born. In those days people believed that such information could reveal details about a person's character and future. Yet even Copernicus's horoscope could not have predicted the enormous ways in which his work and discoveries would one day change our understanding of the stars and planets.

As a young boy Copernicus loved to be outdoors. In the winter he skated on the frozen river near his home. In the summer he ran, played games on the grass, and went horseback riding. He had two older sisters and an older brother for company. Copernicus's father was a talented businessman, and his mother belonged to one of the richest families in Poland. Copernicus's parents were able to provide a nice home and a good education for their children.

Copernicus attended a school that was run by the Roman Catholic Church. His subjects included reading, writing, art, music, and mathematics. Books were very rare in those days. The printing press had just been invented, so few books had been published at the time. Instead of students each having their own books, the teacher read aloud from one book. Students were expected to repeat and memorize the information.

In those days the church made sure that its teachings were strictly followed. Teachers did not encourage students to think for themselves. Instead they expected pupils to repeat what they were taught from the Bible and other books. No one was allowed to disagree with anything that the church said was true.

This image shows Copernicus as a young man. He was an excellent student who had a great desire for knowledge.

Copernicus's uncle, Lucas Watzenrode, would later become a bishop in the Catholic Church.

When Copernicus was about ten years old, his father died. Copernicus and his older sisters and brother became the responsibility of their uncle, Lucas Watzenrode.

Watzenrode was a priest in the Roman Catholic Church. He was a very strict and serious man. He was also very rich and highly respected in the community.

Copernicus and his **siblings** were well provided for by their uncle. Watzenrode wanted to make sure that they found respectable positions in the community. In those days girls did not go to college. One of Copernicus's sisters got married and raised a family. His other sister became a nun.

Watzenrode decided that each of his nephews should become a member of the **clergy**, like him. For that, they would need more schooling.

Chapter Two
Higher Education

At age fifteen, Copernicus entered a Roman Catholic high school about 40 miles from his home. He showed a natural ability for understanding scientific ideas. There are reports that while at school he helped a teacher build a sundial for a church. A sundial tells time by measuring the angles of shadows made by the sun as it moves across the sky. Copernicus's help on this project was an early sign that he would one day become an outstanding scientist.

At age eighteen, Copernicus entered the University of Kraków in Poland. He took a variety of courses, including Greek and Latin, mathematics, geometry, and astrology. His favorite subject was astronomy—the study of the stars, planets, and space. Much of the information Copernicus's professors were teaching, however, was wrong.

The University of Kraków is more than 640 years old today. It is still an important university.

In those days most scientists believed that Earth was at the center of the universe. This belief is called the geocentric theory. It says that all the planets, plus the sun, **revolve** around Earth. Scientists claimed that Earth itself did not **rotate**, but rather stood completely still at all times.

Today we know that this information is wrong. However, in Copernicus's day, nobody realized that. They believed the theory of an ancient Egyptian astronomer named Ptolemy. His teachings had been passed down for more than a thousand years.

Ptolemy observed the heavens around the year 150 AD. He was considered one of the greatest astronomers of his time.

To Ptolemy it made perfect sense that Earth was at the center of the universe. After all, people thought human beings were superior to everything else in the world. So where should Earth be but at the center of everything?

Word Roots

The word *geocentric* comes from the Greek word parts *geo*, meaning "earth," and *centric*, meaning "central."

For many centuries astronomers offered "proof" that Ptolemy's geocentric theory was true. Every morning they saw the sun appear in the east. They watched it move across the sky during the day and settle in the west at night. Clearly the sun had to orbit Earth, they said.

Astronomers also watched the moon and stars move across the sky at night. The five planets known at the time—Mercury, Venus, Mars, Jupiter, and Saturn—could be seen crossing the sky as well. All this was further proof, scientists claimed, that everything revolved around Earth.

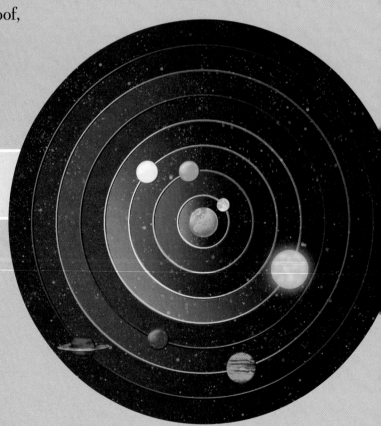

This image illustrates the geocentric theory.

Astronomers did not realize that air and clouds were trapped in Earth's atmosphere.

Astronomers also gave reasons to "prove" that Earth stood still. They argued that if Earth was turning, people would feel the motion and would get dizzy. Furthermore, they claimed, people would be **flung** off the planet into space if Earth spun.

Astronomers also argued that if Earth traveled in space, birds and clouds in the air would be left behind. What would keep them from floating off as Earth raced around the sun? Scientists decided that the best explanation was that Earth didn't move at all.

However, not every part of Ptolemy's theory had an easy answer. Some aspects continued to **perplex** astronomers for centuries. People noticed that Mars and the other planets sometimes made backward loops in the sky. It was odd that they seemed to change direction while circling Earth. Ptolemy's theory offered explanations for these kinds of problems, but each answer made his theory more and more complex.

In college Copernicus spent long hours learning as much about astronomy as he could. He read many ancient texts that were written in Greek and Latin. He found that some scientists of long ago had different ideas about the way the planets and the sun were positioned in the sky.

One book that Copernicus discovered described the beliefs of an ancient Greek astronomer named Aristarchus. He taught that the planets and the sun do not revolve around Earth. Rather, Aristarchus said, all the planets—including Earth—revolve around the sun. This belief is called the heliocentric theory.

This image illustrates the heliocentric theory.

Word Roots

The word *heliocentric* comes from the Greek word parts *helio*, meaning "sun," and *centric*, meaning "central."

In this illustration Copernicus holds a flower called lily of the valley, a symbol of the medical profession at the time.

The more Copernicus read and the more that he saw while watching the sky, the more he felt the geocentric theory didn't quite make sense. Copernicus, being open-minded, wondered if the teachings of Aristarchus could possibly be correct.

Copernicus remained in college for several years. He studied a variety of subjects, including math, astronomy, and medicine. He spent four years studying in Kraków and then another few years at the University of Bologna in Italy. To prepare for a job in the clergy, he earned a degree in church law.

In 1501 Copernicus left Italy and went home to work for the church. But he longed to keep learning, so he soon left home for another university in Italy. It was not until 1506 that Copernicus finished his studies. By then he had an impressive range of knowledge in many subjects. Through all these years he had continued to study astronomy. His **passion** for the stars would stay with him his whole life.

Chapter Three
New Ideas

Copernicus began to work at two different careers. As a clergyman, he served in the Frauenberg Cathedral in Poland, leading religious services and collecting taxes for the church. He also used his medical training to practice as a doctor.

Copernicus lived at the cathedral. His room was in a high tower near the top of the building. From there he had a clear, wide view of the sky.

Copernicus worked very hard during the day. At night he continued to **pursue** his favorite activity—gazing at and studying the heavens. The only tools available at the time were simple instruments that allowed him to measure the position of objects in the distant sky.

The Frauenberg Cathedral was a very tall structure for the time.

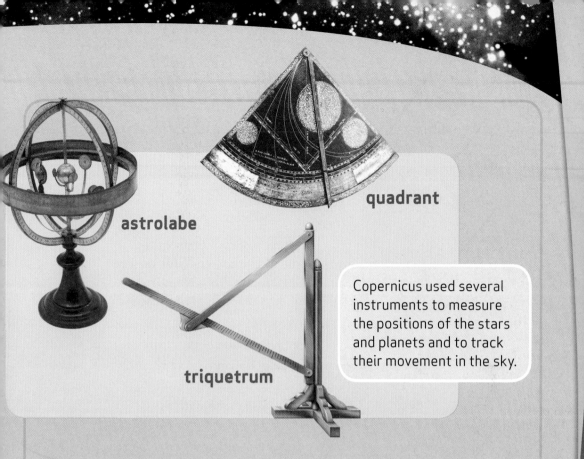

astrolabe

quadrant

triquetrum

Copernicus used several instruments to measure the positions of the stars and planets and to track their movement in the sky.

As he studied objects in the sky, Copernicus kept notebooks in which he recorded the sights he saw and the thoughts that puzzled him. One night in 1512 he noted that Mars was making one of its strange backward loops. Rather than ignore it, he became determined to discover what caused the planet to travel that way.

Finally Copernicus hit upon a possible explanation. What if Mars wasn't really moving backward at all? What if Earth was just passing it somehow? If Earth was moving faster than Mars, then Mars would get farther and farther behind. Mars would look like it was traveling backward! Copernicus knew that this was more than just a good answer to his question about Mars. If he was right, it would mean that Earth did not stand still. Proving his explanation would change astronomy forever.

Aristarchus's beliefs angered some of the ancient Greeks. One philosopher wrote a book arguing that Aristarchus should be arrested.

Copernicus realized that his explanation for the backward movement of Mars agreed with the ideas of Aristarchus. The Greek astronomer had said that Earth and other planets travel around the sun. Copernicus used this explanation to figure out that Earth was closer to the sun than Mars was and that it moved in a smaller, faster circle. That was why Earth kept passing Mars.

With that understanding, Copernicus began to solve more puzzles about the sky. The sun appeared to travel across the sky not because it was moving, but because Earth was spinning. To a person who is spinning around, everything else looks like it is moving, even though it really may not be moving at all.

In time Copernicus developed more ideas based on his observations. He figured out that Earth completes one rotation a day and orbits the sun once a year. His research also helped establish that Earth rotates on its own axis.

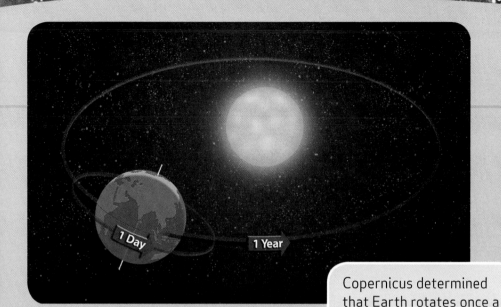

1 Day

1 Year

Copernicus determined that Earth rotates once a day and revolves around the sun once a year.

Copernicus recalled the "proofs" that his professors had offered in college to support the idea that Earth did not move. They had argued that people would feel dizzy or fall off Earth if it rotated. Copernicus believed that Earth's motion was a natural part of life. He believed that people travel along with Earth. He also believed that the birds and clouds in the air did not drift off because the air that surrounds Earth moves along with it.

Earth's Axis

Imagine that a ball is spinning on your desk. If that ball were Earth, the very top would be the North Pole, and the very bottom would be the South Pole. The axis of Earth is the imaginary line from one pole to the other. Copernicus figured out that Earth's axis is on a tilt. It tilts in the same direction no matter where the sun is.

Chapter Four
Producing Books

Eventually Copernicus made enough observations of the stars and planets to decide the heliocentric theory was correct. He wrote a booklet that explained that the planets revolve around the sun, not around Earth. He also stated that Earth spins, which is why the sun, stars, and planets *seem* to move around Earth.

Copernicus called his booklet *Little Commentary*. He knew the church would be unhappy with his writings. The church believed Earth was the center of the universe. Anyone who believed differently could be badly punished. Because Copernicus worked for the church, his ideas could make them even angrier and put his job in danger.

Copernicus decided not to have the booklet published. Instead he wrote out several copies by hand and shared them with only a few close friends.

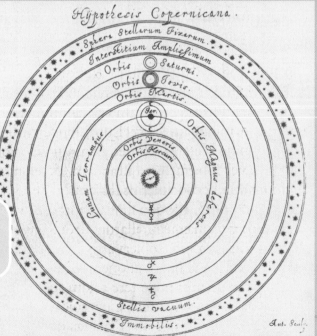

This heliocentric diagram was made in the sixteenth century. It is labeled with Latin writing.

In Copernicus's time, people who did not agree with the Roman Catholic Church were often taken to courts and treated like criminals.

After writing his booklet, Copernicus began working on a much longer book about astronomy. He continued to view the stars and planets and to record what he saw. He spent the next 29 years writing down his findings. In the final two years of his research, Copernicus worked with a German mathematics professor named George Rheticus. Copernicus and his heliocentric theory fascinated Rheticus.

In 1541 Copernicus finally finished his new book. He called it *On the Revolutions of the Heavenly Spheres*. By now he was sixty-eight years old and in poor health. He wasn't sure if the book should be published and widely **distributed**. He feared that his writings would anger the church. He also had a new worry: What if his ideas were wrong after all?

But Rheticus convinced him to publish the book. He thought Copernicus's ideas were too important to keep them a secret from the world. Eventually Copernicus agreed.

Unfortunately the book was not printed the way Copernicus wrote it. An important religious leader named Osiander managed the book's printing, and he made some of his own decisions. Osiander worried about Copernicus's challenging ideas, so he wrote his own introduction, or beginning, and slipped it into the book. Osiander's introduction stated that the book described an imaginary model of the planets and should not be taken as fact.

The book was finally published on May 24, 1543. By then Copernicus was on his deathbed. The first printed copy of the book was brought to him just a few hours before he died at the age of seventy.

Copernicus's book was first printed at a press in Nuremberg, Germany. Only a few hundred copies were printed.

Chapter Five
Supporting Copernicus

At first Copernicus's new book had little effect on the world of science. Most astronomers—as well as church officials—continued to argue that Copernicus's heliocentric theory was wrong. They pointed to the book's introduction, which stated that the book shouldn't be taken seriously. Not until more than 50 years later was it discovered that Copernicus had not actually written the printed introduction.

Over the following years other astronomers came to agree—through their own observations—that Copernicus's ideas were indeed correct. Unfortunately some individuals who agreed with Copernicus paid with their lives. In 1600 an Italian professor named Giordano Bruno was killed in Rome for teaching Copernicus's heliocentric theory.

Giordano Bruno

By 1609 astronomers had a new instrument for observing the stars and planets. It was the **telescope**. It made the heavenly bodies appear larger for astronomers who viewed them from Earth.

The first astronomer to use a telescope was Galileo Galilei of Italy. He saw large objects in space that had never been seen before. They included four bright moons **reflecting** sunlight as they traveled around Jupiter. His discovery proved that not all heavenly bodies traveled around Earth, as Ptolemy had said.

Galileo continued to use his telescope. He made more discoveries about the planets that gave added support to Copernicus's heliocentric theory.

Eventually Galileo was put on trial and forced to say that he no longer believed in Copernicus's ideas. Galileo was imprisoned in his home for the rest of his life.

Galileo wrote about three characters discussing the heliocentric theory. The church made him include the geocentric theory too.

New Planets, New Years

In Copernicus's day astronomers knew of only five planets in addition to Earth. They were Mercury, Venus, Mars, Jupiter, and Saturn. Today we know of two more planets in our solar system—Uranus and Neptune.

We also know how long it takes each planet to orbit the sun. The farther a planet is from the sun, the longer it takes to orbit. The farthest planets have the largest circles to complete. The bar graph below shows how long it takes for each planet to orbit the sun.

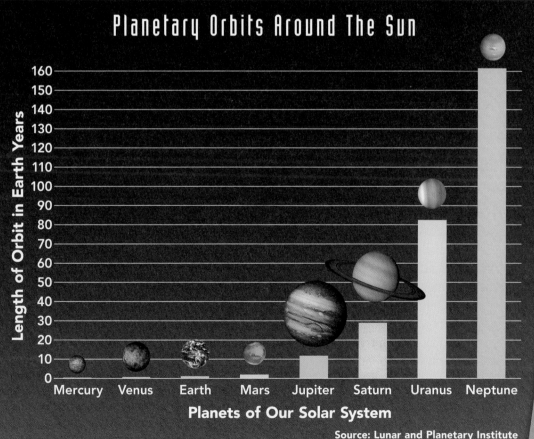

Planetary Orbits Around The Sun

Length of Orbit in Earth Years

Planets of Our Solar System

Source: Lunar and Planetary Institute

After Copernicus died it took about 150 years before most astronomers admitted that his heliocentric theory was correct. The person who managed to convince them was an English scientist named Isaac Newton. He spent many years studying how the world is held together. He became famous for his studies on the pulling force known as **gravity**.

In 1687 Newton published a book that described many of his scientific findings. He explained that the planets are held in their paths in the sky by the pull of the sun—its gravity. He said that Earth, too, orbits the sun and is held by the sun's gravity. Newton's findings convinced astronomers that Earth rotates on its axis and revolves around the sun.

A popular story states that Newton came up with his theory of gravity after watching an apple fall from a tree and land on the ground.

Astronauts today can see the planets from the viewpoint of space.

In 1962 an astronaut named John Glenn became the first American to orbit Earth in a rocket. He was able to witness first-hand that Copernicus was right: Earth rotates on its axis and revolves around the sun. Copernicus's heliocentric theory helped change the way we think about the universe. It showed scientists that while Earth is precious, it is not at the center of the stars.

Because of Copernicus, we explore space today with a better understanding of Earth's place in the universe. Our huge telescopes and powerful rockets expand upon the ideas that he first published centuries ago. However, Copernicus made his discoveries with only math, science, and his observations to guide him. His greatest tool was the power of his mind.

Think Back
Selection 1

Focus Question: What patterns and cycles do we find in space?

A ## Check Understanding ★

Make a list of the patterns and cycles Nicolaus Copernicus found while studying space.

PRACTICE COMPANION **293**

B ## Understand Text Features ★★

Look at the bar graph on page 25. Show the bar graph to a partner. Explain what information in the text the graph helps you understand.

C ## Share and Compare ★★

Compare your list of patterns and cycles with a partner's list. Are any of the patterns and cycles the same? Are any different? Explain why.

D ## Think Critically ★★★★

Why do people study space? Use examples from the selection to explain.

My Home Page

Think Ahead
Selection 2

Focus Question: How did people of the past explain objects in the night sky?

Selection Connection

You have learned about the kinds of discoveries scientists made about patterns and cycles in space. In the next selection you will learn why people study space.

Show What You Know

Think about the following: *the moon*, *the stars*, and *the sky at night*. Do you know any stories about these things? Write your ideas. PRACTICE COMPANION 294

Preview

How did people of the past explain objects in the night sky? Preview pages 30–53. Then read *Oh My Stars!* to find out.

Oh My Stars!

by Karen Baicker

Chapter 1 > History of the Stars

Have you ever stood outside on a dark, clear night and tried to find patterns in the stars? You probably noticed that some stars are bright, while others look like distant **specks**. You probably also noticed that it can be difficult to find order in the stars.

Whatever patterns we do see, though, are the same as they were 10,000 years ago. In ancient days people knew many stars quite well. They kept track of the constellations, or groups and patterns of stars. They gave constellations names. The word *astronomy*, which is the study of stars and planets, comes from two Greek words that mean "star" and "to arrange."

People made up stories about the constellations. Some were based on gods, folktales, and animals. People in Greece had one set of stories. People in Rome and Egypt had others. Most stories you hear today about constellations probably come from ancient Greece.

ORION

Betelgeuse

Rigel

Star Stories

One of the most interesting constellations looks like a hunter
with a bright belt and a sword. The Greeks named this group of
stars Orion, the Hunter. Orion's belt is made up of three bright
stars called blue supergiants because of their slightly bluish tint
and their size. Each star is hotter and much more massive than
our sun. The bright red star on Orion's shoulder is Betelgeuse.
Betelgeuse is about 15 times the size of our sun. Rigel, the
gleaming blue star at the bottom, is Orion's foot.

The position of the constellation of Orion in the sky makes it
possible for people to see it from almost any place on Earth. We
can all look for the hunter as he roams through the sky at night.

The constellation Gemini, which means "Twins," has two bright stars. Interestingly, the stars were seen as twins by several ancient cultures. To Arabs they were twin peacocks. Egyptians called them twin goats. The Hindus called them twin horsemen.

To the Greeks one twin was known as Castor, and the other was Pollux. The brothers shared adventures and were very close. When Castor died, Pollux couldn't bear to be without his brother, so he asked the god Zeus to take away his life too. Zeus placed the twins in the sky as a memorial to brotherly love.

One of the largest constellations is known as Centaurus. A centaur is a mythical creature that has the upper body of a man and the body and legs of a horse. The constellation honors a centaur who taught the children of the gods. Centaurus includes Alpha Centauri, one of the brightest stars we can see in the sky.

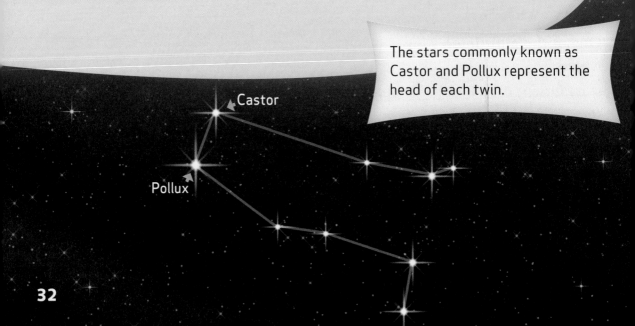

The stars commonly known as Castor and Pollux represent the head of each twin.

Castor

Pollux

This painting reflects the importance of crops and harvests to the ancient Egyptians.

Seasonal Star Patterns

Ancient people studied the stars continuously. In every culture people kept charts of the skies, drew diagrams, and watched for changes. They noticed over time that the sun, the moon, and the stars repeated certain patterns. The different patterns or positions of the stars matched the changing of seasons.

Studying the patterns of the stars allowed people to make predictions about the seasons. In ancient Egypt, for example, when the star Sirius was in a certain place in the sky, people knew the Nile River would soon flood. That knowledge helped people figure out when to plant and harvest their crops.

Guided by Starlight

Studying the stars also proved useful for figuring out directions on Earth. The stars provided a kind of map. At night people could tell where they were and which direction to travel once they located certain familiar stars. For example, people could determine which way was north by locating Polaris, the North Star, which is in the sky directly above the North Pole.

Star maps were invaluable at sea. In the daytime sailors used the position and movement of the sun, but imagine being on a vast ocean in the dark with no paths or landmarks. At night the stars would be the only visible objects to help you know where you were. Sailors learned to use stars to **navigate**. The North Star was a guiding point of light and could always be counted on to be in the northern sky. Star patterns, such as the Big Dipper, always appeared in certain parts of the sky at certain times, so they too were guiding lights. They were a sailor's most important tool. People could sail for thousands of miles using only the stars to map their course.

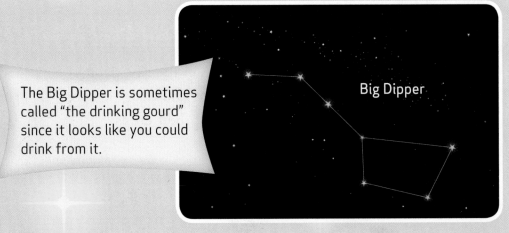

The Big Dipper is sometimes called "the drinking gourd" since it looks like you could drink from it.

Big Dipper

For thousands of years people gathered information about the skies just by using their eyes to observe carefully. Ancient people even established early **observatories**, which are structures or places set up to watch the moon, stars, and planets. People recorded data they gathered by carving it onto clay tablets. As centuries passed, scientists began to make special tools to measure the positions of the stars with greater detail.

Stonehenge in England is believed by some to be an ancient astronomical observatory.

Astrolabe

One of the first and most beautiful instruments made to study the sky was invented over 2,000 years ago. The astrolabe could be called a mechanical map of the sky. Its movable parts and its symbols and numbers are used to find a star or planet. The astrolabe uses the position of the sun or stars to tell the time of day or night. It can even tell when sunrise and sunset will be. A simplified form of the tool was used to help sailors navigate the seas. Astrolabes were widely used in many parts of the world until the middle of the 1600s. Then new instruments were developed.

Astrolabes were used to mark the changing positions of the stars.

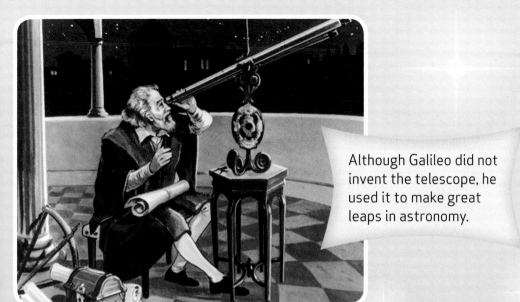

Although Galileo did not invent the telescope, he used it to make great leaps in astronomy.

Telescope

When the telescope was first invented in the early 1600s, its possibilities were untested. The Italian scientist Galileo was among the first to turn a telescope skyward. Ancient Greeks knew the moon revolved around Earth and that moonlight was reflected sunlight. What Galileo discovered with the telescope was that the moon was not smooth, which is what people first thought. He described amazing **lunar** features such as tall mountains and large craters.

Galileo also saw that there were thousands more stars in the sky than people could see with their unaided eyes. As telescopes became more powerful, millions and millions more stars could be seen.

Observations with the telescope supported the idea that the sun, not Earth, was the center of the universe. It took many years and the work of great thinkers like Copernicus and Newton for people to **comprehend** and accept these ideas about the solar system.

More Tools to Study the Skies

People used a number of other tools to study and track the stars. These tools all measure the distance of a star or the sun from the horizon. The tools could be used to map stars or to help people navigate the seas. For navigation, once the distance to the horizon is known, a sailor can figure out the ship's location.

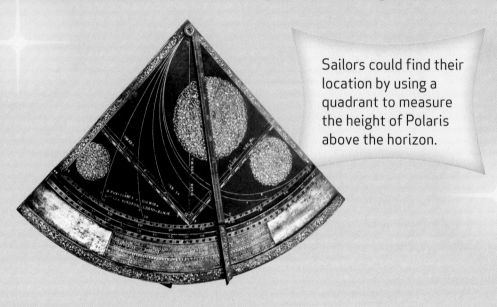

Sailors could find their location by using a quadrant to measure the height of Polaris above the horizon.

Like the quadrant, the cross-staff measured the position of a particular star above the horizon.

The back-staff was an improvement over the cross-staff. Its user could measure the height of the sun above the horizon with his or her back to the sun.

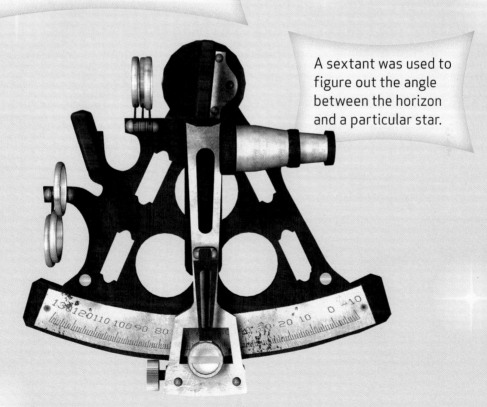

A sextant was used to figure out the angle between the horizon and a particular star.

The sun is a star.

Chapter 3 — Star Facts

Even though people continued to find ways to gather information from stars, they still did not know what stars actually are. Today we know that a star is more than just a twinkling spot of light in the sky.

A star is an **immense**, shining ball of hot gas. Stars you see at night are trillions of miles away. That's why they appear as tiny points of light—even through a powerful telescope. In fact many stars are much bigger and brighter than our sun. The sun appears larger and brighter because it is much closer to Earth than any other star—a mere 93 million miles away!

Light Years Away

When you look at a star, you are not seeing it as it exists at that moment. You are seeing what it looked like many years ago. That's because stars are so far away that their light takes a long time to reach Earth. For example, when you look at Sirius, you are looking

After the sun, Sirius is the brightest star in the sky.

at the way the star looked about eight years ago! If you're ten years old, the light you see started its trip when you were two!

Until the 1670s people did not know how fast light traveled. A scientist named Olaus Roemer became the first person to measure the speed of light. He made his measurements by studying the moons of the planet Jupiter. Roemer's measurement of the speed of light was close to its actual measurement today.

We know now that light travels very quickly. It travels more than 186,000 miles per second, in fact. But it still takes time to reach a planet 25 trillion miles away! So scientists measure distance in light-years, or how far light travels in one year. A light year is about six trillion miles. If light from an old star has traveled many light years, you might even be looking at a star that no longer exists!

Studying the Life of a Star

People once thought stars lasted forever. Stars do last millions to billions of years, but not forever. Today we know stars have complex life cycles.

The life of a star begins within a giant cloud of hydrogen gas and dust called a nebula. Over a period of millions of years, gravity pulls more of the gas together. The cloud of gas begins to spin and produce heat. As it gets hotter, a process called nuclear fusion happens. The cloud starts to glow brightly. Eventually a star is born!

A star remains stable for 90 percent of its life. It continues to glow, burning its hydrogen gas. When the gas runs low, its core begins to **collapse** but its outer layers expand. The outer layers "cool" to a red glow. Depending on a star's size, it becomes a red giant or red supergiant toward the end of its life cycle.

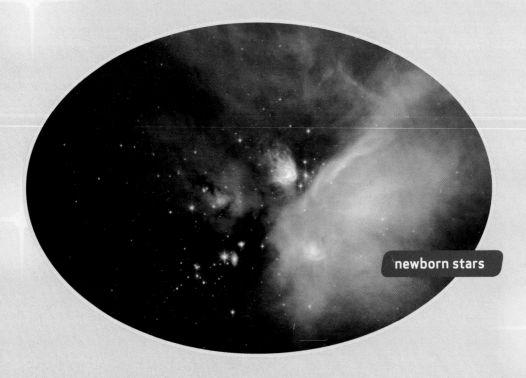

newborn stars

How do scientists know these details about the life cycle of a star? They have created better and better instruments to study stars.

Huge, high-powered telescopes are placed in observatories on Earth. The observatories are on mountains, far away from city lights. Observatory domes open up, allowing scientists to **gaze** at stars many light years away.

Other telescopes, such as the Hubble Telescope, move around Earth in space. They take pictures of stars millions of light years away and send them back to Earth. Scientists have been able to observe gases and dust that are forming new stars. They've seen stars in the last stages of life. Their observations have proven that stars do indeed have life cycles.

The Keck Observatory in Hawaii has two of the largest telescopes on Earth.

Star Types

Scientists have learned more and more about what a star's size and color tell about its life cycle. Telescope images have helped scientists classify types of stars. Here are some you might see in the night sky.

Red Dwarfs

Red dwarfs are the most common type of star in the universe. They are less than half the size of the sun. Their red or orange color tells us the surface temperatures are relatively cool. They burn their fuel slowly. They're dim and hard to see, but they may live for about 100 billion years!

Red Supergiants

A star must be five times larger than the sun to become a red supergiant. Betelgeuse is one. In earlier phases, these stars follow the same pattern as medium-sized stars. In the red supergiant phase, the outer layers are brighter and cooler. The light is as bright as 100 billion stars! Eventually they explode, forming a supernova.

White Dwarfs

In the life cycle of a medium-sized star, such as the sun, the white dwarf phase follows the red giant phase. The core's energy and the pull of gravity get out of balance. The glowing red outer layer is blown away. The core collapses further. What is left is a white dwarf. It may be only a couple hundred miles wide, but it shines with a white-hot light—until it dies.

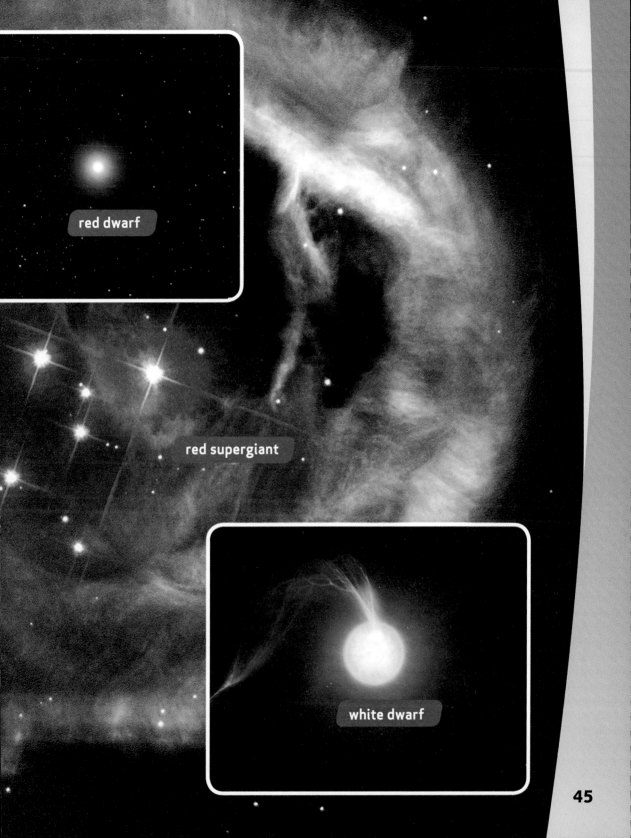

red dwarf

red supergiant

white dwarf

Star Words

"Twinkle twinkle little star
How I wonder what you are!"

Over the years, countless children have fallen asleep each night to the words of this nursery rhyme. In fact, wondering about the stars and what they are has inspired many poems, songs, and stories.

The stars are suspended on strings that are pulled up in the daytime and let down at night.
     —Babylonian mythology, 3000 B.C.

"Star Light, Star Bright
First star I see tonight.
I wish I may, I wish I might
Have the wish I wish tonight."
     —Anonymous

"For my part, I declare I know nothing whatever about it, but to look at the stars always makes me dream."
     —Vincent van Gogh, painter (1853–1890)

Stars

Alone in the night
On a dark hill
With pines around me
Spicy and still,

And a heaven full of stars
Over my head,
White and topaz
And misty red;

Myriads with beating
Hearts of fire
That aeons
Cannot vex or tire;

Up the dome of heaven
Like a great hill,
I watch them marching
Stately and still,

And I know that I
Am honored to be
Witness
Of so much majesty.

—Sarah Teasdale, poet (1884–1933)

Today's sky map seems so much bigger than when constellations were first mapped. We now know there are different types of stars, such as white dwarfs and red giants. We also know there are trillions of stars. Scientists have detected new solar systems and galaxies surrounding some of these stars. Each time scientists discover a star, it tells us more about what makes up our universe.

Solar Systems

Solar means "of the sun." A solar system is made up of a star and any planets and other objects that orbit the star. At the center of our own solar system is the sun. Orbiting around our sun are eight planets, including Earth, and more than 100 moons. Many smaller objects such as dwarf planets, meteoroids, and comets orbit the sun in a solar system.

Astronomers have discovered that about 50 distant stars also have planets orbiting them. They can't see the planets, but they know the planets are there.

Galaxies

A solar system is part of a galaxy. Like solar systems, galaxies are held together by the pull of gravity and contain a collection of stars, gases, and dust. Our solar system is in the galaxy called the Milky Way. Other than the Milky Way, only three galaxies can be seen without a telescope. They are no more than two million light years from Earth.

It is only very recently that people realized there are galaxies far beyond ours. There may be more than 100 billion galaxies in the visible universe.

The Milky Way appears to be a milky white path across the night sky.

The Universe

All of the solar systems and galaxies are within the universe. It is made up of everything that is found anywhere in space.

How far does the universe reach? No one knows for sure how big it is. But scientists have realized that the universe itself is getting bigger. It's growing, like a balloon being blown up. Other galaxies are now farther away from us than they once were.

Up to the mid-1950s, most people **assumed** there was one universe. However, some astronomers have since wondered if there might be more than one. If you imagine blowing a number of soap bubbles instead of blowing up one balloon, you can picture one idea of multiple universes.

The Andromeda Galaxy is known as a spiral galaxy because of the shape the stars form. It is roughly 2.5 million light years away from Earth.

Astronomers are always finding new ways to explore and explain new parts of the universe. They send space shuttles with telescopes and cameras into outer space. They measure light waves from distant stars. They also use computers to help figure out data. Computers do many of the math problems that help astronomers understand the universe.

In whatever way they can, scientists look as deeply into space as technology will allow, just as the scientists of years ago did. New technology continues to shed new light on stars and the universe every year.

Sum It Up

People have always been curious about the stars. When ancient people could only see stars unaided by technology, they wrote stories, rhymes, and songs about them. We still look for constellations and write about the stars today.

For centuries farmers and sailors relied on star patterns to tell time, to foreshadow seasons, and to help them find their way. Today we typically don't rely on the stars in these ways, but we do study them to learn more about the universe. We use our knowledge of light years and of the life cycles of these brilliant stars to tell us about the history of the universe. From the first simple telescope and observatories to the advanced forms we have today, technology has helped us learn more about stars. We now rocket technology out of Earth's atmosphere to view our solar system, to see distant galaxies, and to look into the far reaches of the universe.

Just like people of ancient times, we still use our imaginations to think about the universe. And we continue to develop technology that will move us beyond what is visible today. Who knows? We might locate another universe!

BETELGEUSE

ALDEBARAN

5 JUN 20

PROCYON

CAPELLA

10 JUL 20 25

POLLUX

Northern Horizon Circle

Ecliptic

5

10 AUG 20

REGULUS

25

POLARIS

5

10 SEP 20

25

A sky chart like this changes during the year because of Earth's location in its orbit around the sun.

ARCTURUS

SPICA

OCT

25

Think Back
Selection 2

A Check Understanding ★

How did people of the past explain stars in the night sky? How do their ideas differ from what we know now?

PRACTICE COMPANION **310**

B Understand Text Features ★★

An index is an alphabetical list of subjects found at the back of a book. Page numbers help you find the subjects within the book. Using the index, where would you find information about the telescope? Share your information with a partner.

C Share and Compare ★★

Make a list of past ideas about objects in space. Compare your list with a partner's list. Which ideas are the same? Which are different? Why?

D Think Critically ★★★★

Why do people study space? Use examples from the selection to explain.

Selection Connection

You have learned how people of the past were inspired by the night sky. In the next selection you will learn why people study space.

Show What You Know

Think about the following: *telescopes*, *satellites*, and *space vehicles*. How do these things help us view space? Write your ideas.

PRACTICE COMPANION **311**

Preview ▶   onl ne coach

How do people view space today?
Preview pages 56–77. Then read *The Brain and the Movie* to find out.

The Brain and the Movie

by Larry Wallberg

Illustrated by Mark and Rosemary Jarman

chapter one
No Parts for Young Girls

You might think that having a famous actress for a mother would be wonderful for a kid. Most of the time you would be absolutely correct. But once in a while, having a well-known star for a parent can drive you bananas!

I should know, because my mother happens to be the international celebrity Rhonda Reva. You must have seen her in dozens of movies, and I'm guessing that you adored her in every single one of them. And why not? She's talented and beautiful and smart.

I definitely have no talents that I know of, because I can't dance and I can't sing and I'm even lousy at sports.

I'm not sure I'm beautiful, but people say I look like my mother when she was my age. She keeps telling me that when I get older, I'll grow into my looks, which makes me sound like a girl whose face is twice the size of her body. Which it isn't!

But I'm certainly smart. In fact, there are some subjects I know a lot more about than my mother does. She calls me Brain, even though my name is Flora, because I'm kind of a **genius** in science and math. I'm particularly interested in space technology.

So imagine how excited I became when my mother and I were eating dinner one night and she said, "I'm going to be in a science fiction movie."

Now I had never asked my mother anything like this before, but when I heard the movie was going to take place in outer space, I found it impossible to resist. "Can I be in it too?"

Mom stared at me as if I had two heads, which would have been great if there was a part in the movie for a two-headed monster. I guess there wasn't, because she said, "Sorry, Brain, but there are no parts in this movie for young girls. Plus, you've never acted before! I'm not sure your first time should be in a big movie."

"Does the movie have any space technology in it?" I asked.

"I think so," Mom said. "The story is about a group of astronauts who are going to explore a planet discovered by some well-known telescope that revolves around Earth."

I knew right away that she had to be talking about the Hubble Space Telescope, and I got even more excited than I was before.

"I really should be in that movie!" I exclaimed. "I'll bet I know more about the Hubble than any of the actors in the picture. I also know about the Spitzer Space Telescope, and the Chandra X-ray Observatory, and . . ."

"Sure," Mom said with a chuckle, "I'm positive that you do. But we actors aren't required to know anything about science. We just read the lines that the screenwriter wrote into the script. If our acting is good, the audience will believe that we know what we're talking about."

"But if I were in the movie, I could share my information with everyone. That would make their performances even better, right?"

"I'm afraid I still have to say no, honey. There just isn't a part for you in this movie."

Mom must have noticed that I was disappointed when I started using my fork to form pictures of telescopes with my macaroni and cheese. I could tell that she felt bad, because she finally blurted out, "If you want, you can come with me tomorrow to our reading."

"What's a reading?" I asked.

"That's when all the actors sit around a big table and read their parts aloud for the first time. You're welcome to come and sit next to me, but you have to promise that you'll be polite to everybody and you won't say anything."

That was an extremely simple promise to make, because I'm always polite, and I never say anything if I'm asked to keep quiet. Well, almost never!

chapter two
The Reading Begins

My mother was the last cast member to arrive at the studio for the reading, so everybody else was already standing around the table and talking when we walked in. She introduced me to Brett Grand, an actor I've admired since I was four years old. I think I must have blushed, because Brett said, "I'm pleased to meet you, Flora. I hope your sunburn doesn't hurt too much."

Then he asked me, "Would you like to be in the movies when you grow up?"

I said, "Actually, I wish I could be in this movie now."

He laughed and patted me on the head. I usually hate it when people do that, but I didn't mind it this time. Brett Grand can pat my head any time he wants!

Then I met Missy Long, who is a **hilarious** comic I know from TV and the movies. I started laughing my head off when I shook her hand, even though she had not said anything funnier than "Hello."

"Well," said Missy, "I'd like to hear what you sound like when I tell a real joke." Then she said "Hello" again, but this time in a silly duck voice, and I cracked up.

There were many other actors there, but I don't remember all their names. I do recall that there was one short, friendly man named Jim, who was going to play a monster on the distant planet. I hope they use lots of makeup when they film his scenes because in real life he's less frightening than a cute kitten!

The director of the movie was named Al Maxfield. He was also the writer of the screenplay. He said to me, "Your mother tells me that you're very interested in space technology, young lady. I think you're going to enjoy this movie."

Then Mr. Maxfield clapped his hands and shouted, "All right you **magnificent** bunch of people, take your seats." When all the actors had made themselves comfortable around the table, Mr. Maxfield said, "Let's begin with the first scene."

He explained that my mother was the captain of a spaceship headed from Earth to a distant planet. Brett was the second in command, the chief information officer. Missy was the ship's physician, although I couldn't imagine how sick or injured people could keep from giggling when she tried to treat them.

Brett read his first line. "We have just passed the moon, Captain, and if you look out your left window, you'll be able to see the Hubble telescope as we approach it."

I guess I must have been so surprised that I spoke without realizing what I was doing. "Wait a minute, Mr. Grand," I said. "Could you read that again?"

My mother **nudged** me under the table and whispered, "You promised you wouldn't say anything, Brain."

"But I have to, Mom," I whispered back. "Mr. Grand just read something that doesn't make any logical sense at all."

Brett repeated his line exactly the same way.

My mother rolled her eyes and said, "Excuse me, Brett and Al and everybody else, but my daughter wishes to make a comment about the script."

Everyone looked at me curiously, waiting to hear what I had to say.

"Well," I began, "if you were traveling from Earth, you would never pass the moon and *then* look for the Hubble telescope. The Hubble is much, much closer to Earth than the moon is. On average the moon is about 239,000 miles from Earth, but the Hubble telescope is only about 370 miles away."

"Are you positive?" asked Mr. Maxfield.

I nodded and then said, "Sorry."

"There's nothing to be sorry about, young lady," said Mr. Maxfield. "We'll just have to fix that line and have the crew spot the Hubble telescope *before* they pass the moon. Thanks for the information."

Then Mr. Maxfield turned to Brett Grand and said, "Just skip that sentence for now. Start reading again, beginning with the line right after that one."

Brett read, "We'd better keep our fingers crossed that our rocket is built as well as the Hubble telescope was. It's an amazing instrument. Did you know that it has been orbiting Earth for over two decades, but it has never been changed from its original design and has never had to be repaired?"

I'm afraid I groaned.

My mother whispered, "Just let the man read his lines, Flora."

"I can't," I said out loud. I guess I should have whispered, but I forgot. "That information is totally wrong. Imagine all the kids in the audience of this movie, hearing incorrect facts."

"Um . . . have you found another **minor** error, Flora?" asked Al Maxfield.

I didn't think it was minor at all, but I said, "Yes. Some of the Hubble telescope's parts have been replaced, and it has been fixed a number of times. It was launched in 1990, but it required some work in 1993. After that, it was fixed a few more times. In May 2009 it was repaired for the fifth time!"

"Are you positive?" asked Mr. Maxfield again.

"Of course she's positive," said my mother. "You don't think she's making this stuff up, do you?"

"Oh, all right," said Mr. Maxfield. "I'll amend that line too. Let's just say that the Hubble is an amazing instrument because it has been brought back to Earth for repairs only a few times."

I didn't mean to, but I smacked myself on the side of my head when I heard that.

Missy seemed interested. "Please don't hurt your head, Flora, but that's wrong too, isn't it?" she asked me. "They can't just put that huge thing in a bag and bring it home to a telescope-fixing shop, can they?"

I laughed. "Well, it weighs more than 12 tons, which is about twice the weight of an average male African elephant. And it's approximately the size of a big school bus. So no, it certainly wouldn't fit in a regular bag."

"Then how do they fix it?" Missy asked.

"Astronauts fly up there on a space shuttle," I explained. "When they get to the telescope, some of them do a spacewalk. They carry tools and parts over to the Hubble."

"Do they need those funny suits?" asked Missy.

"Of course," I said. "The suit is specially designed to keep the air pressure and the temperature at levels that the astronauts need to survive. It also has a life-support system so they can breathe, and even places to keep food and drink in case they need a snack while they work."

Then Missy said to Al Maxfield, "Don't you think I'd be hilarious if I wore one of those big, bulky suits in this movie? I could say that I'll never get a date if I have to dress in those clothes. Maybe you should write a scene where I do a spacewalk."

Mr. Maxfield said, "Let's just get back to reading the script. Later I'll fix all those lines about repairing the telescope. Whose character speaks next?"

My mother said, "Mine does," and began reading. "Thanks to the Hubble, we can see faraway planets, like the one we're going to explore. It's fortunate for us," she read, "that the Hubble goes around Earth twice each day and can take photographs of objects a few thousand miles away."

She hesitated for a second before asking me, "Is that right, Flora?"

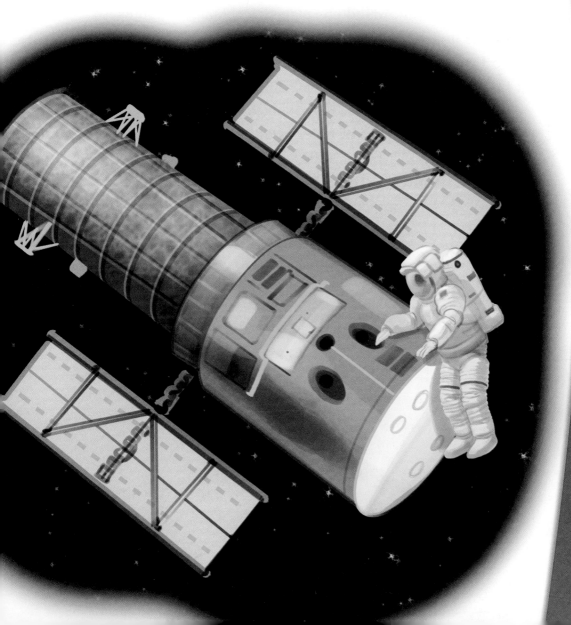

It was a good thing my mother asked me, or I definitely would have lost my self-control and interrupted again, because that last sentence had two completely different mistakes in it.

"Actually, Mom," I said, "it's not correct at all."

"What's wrong with it?" asked Missy.

"First of all, the Hubble doesn't go around Earth just twice each day. It revolves around our planet in about 96 minutes, so that means it orbits Earth about 15 times every 24 hours!"

"So I was off by a little," said Mr. Maxfield, "and I can fix that fact easily enough."

"Secondly," I continued, "the Hubble can take photographs of objects that are *billions* of miles away, not just a few thousand. Nearly 13.7 billion miles, to be exact."

"Are you positive?" asked Mr. Maxfield, yet again.

Everybody sang out loudly, "Yes, she is!"

"You really ought to be in this movie, Flora," Missy said to me, and my heart started racing with excitement. Then she said, "Maybe *you* should have been cast as the chief information officer."

Brett Grand didn't like hearing that. "I beg your pardon," he said to Missy. "I think she should play the ship's doctor." Then he turned to my mother and added, "Or maybe even the captain."

Mr. Maxfield shouted, "I'm not going to make a movie starring some genius kid as a captain, or an information officer, or a ship's doctor, or even a little elf who does spacewalks. This is an adult picture, and there are absolutely no parts for little girls. Sorry, Flora, but that's the way it is."

I guess I must have looked disappointed, because Jim the monster guy came over and offered me some pretzels. My mother gave me **permission** to take some, so I said "thanks" and shoved one in my mouth. Maybe that would keep me silent for a few minutes.

Mr. Maxfield said, "Why don't we skip to a different scene, everyone?"

chapter three
The Raspberry Mistake

Then Mr. Maxfield said, "Turn to page 32 in your scripts, where you'll find the ship's crew discussing a huge dust cloud they're approaching."

My mother began, "We've almost reached the center of the Milky Way."

Missy read, "What's that **formation** up ahead? It looks dangerous."

"It's a gigantic cloud made up of gases and cosmic dust," Brett read. "But it looks like a lot of chocolate and nuts swirled together, so scientists call it the Candy Bar."

That was the most ridiculous thing I'd ever heard, and I must admit that I grunted.

"Is something wrong, Brain?" asked my mother.

"No scientist has ever called a molecular cloud the Candy Bar!" I said. "The ship is most likely nearing Sagittarius B2. That cloud got its name because when you look at it from Earth, it seems to be in the constellation Sagittarius."

"Sajjy-who?" asked Missy.

"The stars in Sagittarius form a picture of a character in Greek mythology," I answered. "Chiron is the character's name, and he was a centaur, a creature with a human's head, chest, and arms, and the body of a horse. He carries a bow and arrow."

"People imagine they can see that when they view the sky?" asked my mother.

"Well," I said, "most people today can't picture a centaur at all, but a smaller part of the constellation looks something like a teapot. Remember, though, that the stars we on Earth use as dots to connect for that image are really millions of miles away from each other."

"Enough with the science lesson," said Mr. Maxfield. "Let's keep reading."

Missy read a funny line. "I hope we keep the windows closed while we travel into that mess. I'd guess it smells like a swamp."

Brett read, "That's absolutely correct."

"That's absolutely *in*correct!" I shouted. "Some scientists think it probably smells like raspberries."

"You're kidding, right?" asked Missy. "How could anyone know what kind of aroma a dust cloud has?"

I smiled and said, "That's a very interesting question, because it has to do with space technology. Scientists use radio telescopes, like the IRAM in Spain, to get signals from objects in space. Those signals can be **analyzed**, and people can tell what kinds of molecules are floating around out there. A molecule is a very small bit of a basic material or chemical."

Brett asked, "Why are they looking at Sagittarius B2?"

I answered, "They're studying Sagittarius B2 because it has a rich stew of many different kinds of molecules found in space."

"So what does that have to do with raspberries?" Missy asked. "Nobody traveled up there to pick fruit, did they?"

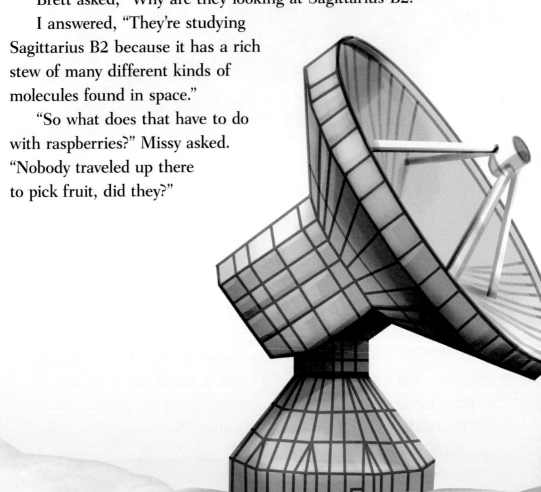

I giggled and answered, "No, but in 2009, scientists discovered some interesting molecules in Sagittarius B2. Those molecules are from the exact same chemical as the one that gives raspberries their taste. So it's possible that the center of the Milky Way smells like raspberries!"

My mother seemed very proud of me as she told everyone, "My daughter reads about space technology all the time. When she gets older, she'll probably become a well-known scientist."

"I still want to be in a movie like this one, though," I said.

Mr. Maxfield said to me, "I'll keep that in mind the next time I write a science fiction script. Maybe I'll even come to you with my writing so you can correct all the mistakes I make."

Everybody laughed loudly at that.

Then Mr. Maxfield clapped his hands and said, "All right, people, it looks as if I'm going to have to rewrite some of the dialogue we've read so far. So now let's go through the last few scenes, the ones that take place on Planet Gamma. Jim, you will read the part of the monster."

chapter four
I'm Older Than I Look!

"Grrrrrrrrr," growled Jim, as **menacingly** as he could, which—as you probably guessed—was not very much.

Mr. Maxfield explained that the cast was about to read a section of the movie that took place on Planet Gamma, in the laboratory of a brilliant scientist who was seventy-seven years old. She had been living on Planet Gamma for many years but recently had become friends with a monster who lived in a cave on the planet. She had tamed the creature so that it listened to everything she said.

"Now," said Mr. Maxfield, "as we begin, the Earth people have just arrived. They have asked the scientist to meet with them because they wish to understand . . ."

Then Mr. Maxfield's mouth and eyes opened wide. He looked really embarrassed. "Hey, wait a minute," he said. "I **regret** to say that I made another mistake. I forgot to find someone to play the seventy-seven-year-old scientist on that planet!"

He turned to me with a desperate look on his face and asked, "Flora, do you think that just today you could read this part aloud until I find someone who's perfect for it?"

I could hardly believe my ears! Naturally I said "Yes!" as quickly as I could. I didn't want to give Mr. Maxfield a chance to change his mind.

There's no way that I can describe exactly how wonderful I felt acting out a scene with my mother and Brett Grand and Missy Long, and even that nice man named Jim. Fortunately I didn't find any mistakes in the scene, mostly because it was pure fantasy. So I didn't have to interrupt myself with any corrections.

The reading went very smoothly, and when we were finished, Mr. Maxfield said, "Thank you very much, Flora." Brett Grand leaned across the table and patted me on the head, Missy Long reached out to shake my hand, my mother kissed me on the cheek, and everyone else in the room gave me a big round of applause.

"I must tell you, Flora, that your reading was absolutely beautiful," said Jim, and I told him that his growling was pretty great too.

Missy tapped Mr. Maxfield on the shoulder and suggested, "Why not just let Flora play that part in the movie?"

When I heard that, I nearly jumped out of my seat to do cartwheels all around the room, but since I don't actually know how to do cartwheels, I stayed in my chair.

Mr. Maxfield looked sad and said, "I agree that Flora would be excellent in the part, but the story needs the scientist to be exactly seventy-seven years old on Planet Gamma. We worked that number into many of the scenes in this movie. We even finished building a giant model of a birthday cake with 77 candles! Nobody who watches the movie would believe that Flora is even half that age, because she looks and sounds like exactly what she is, a very bright and talented young girl who happens to be about nine-and-a-half years old. They would marvel at her knowledge, but they wouldn't understand the plot."

But my brain was already working a mile a minute, and I was adding, subtracting, multiplying, and dividing as quickly as I could. Finally I hollered, "I think I've figured out how I can play a person who's seventy-seven on Planet Gamma!

"The script doesn't mention how long it takes Planet Gamma to revolve around its sun, but let's suppose that it takes 45 Earth days. If that were the case, then I would be seventy-seven on Planet Gamma. I may be nine-and-a-half Earth years, but I'm seventy-seven Gamma years!"

My mother and Missy each wrote some numbers on blank sheets of paper and worked out the problem. Then Mom said, "She's right, Al."

If you happen to see *Adventure on Planet Gamma*, watch for me in the movie. I play the brilliant scientist.

Focus Question: How do people view space today?

A Check Understanding ⭑

Think about the different tools used for space exploration. How do these tools help us get a better view of space today? PRACTICE COMPANION **339**

B Understand Literary Elements ⭑⭑

Imagery is language that describes how someone or something looks, sounds, feels, smells, or tastes. Look for examples of imagery in your selection. Share your examples with a partner.

C Share and Compare ⭑⭑

Make a list of space exploration tools discussed in your selection. Compare your list with a partner's list. Which tools are the same? Which tools are different? Why?

D Think Critically ⭑⭑⭑⭑

Why do people study space? Use examples from the selection to explain.

My Home Page

Think Ahead
Selection 4

Focus Question: How might space be a part of our future?

Selection Connection

In *The Brain and the Movie* you have learned how people view space today. In the next selection you will learn what inspires people to study space.

Show What You Know

Think about the following: *space stations*; *minerals on other planets*; and *traveling to other planets*. How will these help space be a part of our future? Write your ideas.

PRACTICE COMPANION **340**

Preview

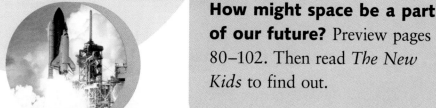

How might space be a part of our future? Preview pages 80–102. Then read *The New Kids* to find out.

The New Kids

by Kathy Zahler
Illustrated by Pixelboy Studios

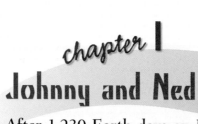

chapter 1
Johnny and Ned

After 1,230 Earth days on Moon Base Nine, the days start to run into one another. There's nothing much new to discover, and every day seems the same as every day that came before. Our teacher, Ms. Anderson, tries hard to find new things to teach us to keep us interested. There are only four of us in the fourth grade, and we're all interested in different things, from rocks to poetry. We're all individuals with very different backgrounds and interests. I think that makes us a challenging class.

That's why all of us, including Ms. Anderson, were so very happy when Johnny and Ned arrived. They were the first kids our age to visit the moon in more than three Earth years. Finally there were more than four of us. They brought with them thrilling stories from the Earth we'd left behind. We could brag to them about our lunar adventures.

I'm getting ahead of the story, though. I suppose I should start at the beginning, which is, of course, where every good story starts.

My name is Jamila, and I came here from Namibia, Africa, with my parents when I was seven years old. We were part of the original crew on Moon Base Nine.

My parents work for the Water Works, which is by far the biggest company on the moon. Since water is now so hard to locate on Earth, even underground, we must instead use the frozen water from the moon, which we ship back to Earth in huge blocks of ice. Spaceships fly back and forth once a week, departing from the port at our base.

I'm just a kid, so naturally I don't have a job. Instead I go to school with Ms. Anderson.

Until Johnny and Ned arrived, Ajani was the only boy in our class. I would have felt strange about that, but Ajani seemed to be perfectly fine with this state of affairs. The other two students, Carmen and Jackie, are girls like me.

I told you that we all like different things, and that is true. I love to write, and I read constantly. I quickly gobbled up all of the children's books in our little base library, and they had to ship new books from Earth every few weeks to keep me busy.

Carmen is a rock hound, which is what you call someone who collects or studies rocks. It makes a lot of sense to be a

rock hound on the moon. There are lots and lots of rocks here. In fact, if I had to use one word to describe the surface of the moon, it would be "rocky," although the term "white-hot" might also apply during daylight.

Ajani is an accomplished artist. His paintings of the moon are especially beautiful. He **illustrates** the way the light changes the face of the moon and how the moon's hills and valleys look as the light moves. He also paints pictures of Earth as we revolve around it. Earth looks shiny and richly blue from up here, and Ajani captures its special beauty in his paintings. I expect that someday his work will hang in Earth museums, and everyone will be able to see what we see from our home on Moon Base Nine.

Jackie is already a fairly famous scientist, although she's only ten years old like the rest of us. She did some studies of the lunar atmosphere that surprised several important scientists on Earth. For a long time people thought that the moon had no atmosphere. Well, it is absolutely true that humans cannot breathe the air here. However, around the moon there is a kind of atmosphere.

Now you see the range of our interests. Ms. Anderson is always trying to find things that will appeal to each of us. She's always coming up with new projects and ideas. She says we're challenging and rewarding.

We live on the side of the moon that always faces Earth. We have bright sunshine here for a couple of Earth weeks, and then we go dark for a couple of Earth weeks. From Earth you would see this change as the cycles of the moon, from a waxing moon to a full moon to a waning moon.

During our long moon day, it gets much hotter than it ever gets on Earth, and during our moon night, it gets far colder than it gets on Earth. Our base is designed to keep us cool during the day and warm during the night. If it weren't designed so well, humans couldn't possibly survive here on the moon.

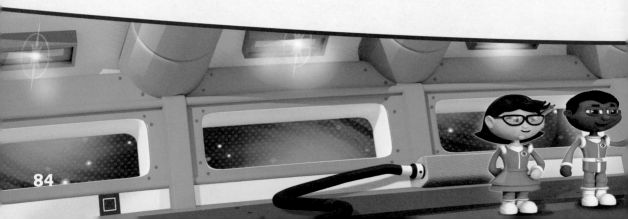

The ship from Earth arrived during our moon day. We all dressed properly and went down to the port to meet the new boys.

Ms. Anderson led us all back to the classroom. You can imagine that we were a little shy. Suppose that you had not met anyone new for more than three years! You would act **bashful** and nervous too, I'm sure.

Ned was very nice. I could tell right away that we would be friends. He was interested in everything about the base. He especially wanted to know how we lived indoors all the time. Back on Earth he was used to a life of outdoor fun—hiking, camping, and riding horses through the dried-up river beds that once held Earth's fresh water. I'd imagine that life on Moon Base Nine would seem a little cramped and uncomfortable for a boy who loved the outdoors.

I told Ned that we did go on field trips from time to time. We put on space suits and were allowed to explore the area around the base. Ned seemed especially interested in that.

I don't want to sound unpleasant or mean, but Johnny was a bit peculiar. He was very polite, but it seemed to me as though he might be trying too hard to be nice. He was a bit of a know-it-all too. Ms. Anderson would say something interesting about the base, and he'd always add facts that he knew. He talked endlessly, in a voice that was slightly annoying—flat and tinny-sounding. Sometimes—well, a lot of the time, frankly—he seemed to know more than we did about the moon! Even Jackie, who is certainly the most intelligent ten-year-old I've ever met, couldn't keep up with Johnny's endless lists of facts. He seemed odd, but I had to get to know him better.

I asked Ned about Johnny. He simply shrugged.

"I met him in training," said Ned. "We hung out together while we worked and learned about the moon. I think he's a fairly cool guy."

Truthfully it didn't matter to me whether Johnny talked a lot; I was just thrilled to meet someone new after spending second and third and most of fourth grade with the same kids. I could easily learn to live with Johnny's funny, flat voice and his endless lists of facts.

I'll admit that within a few Earth days, both Johnny and Ned fit in just fine. Our little class now had six kids, and despite our different interests, we all got along very well. Ned loaned me some books he had brought from Earth. Johnny promised to **assist** me with my math problems. I had two new friends, and I could not have been happier. Even Ms. Anderson seemed to have perked up. Life at Moon Base Nine was improving by the day.

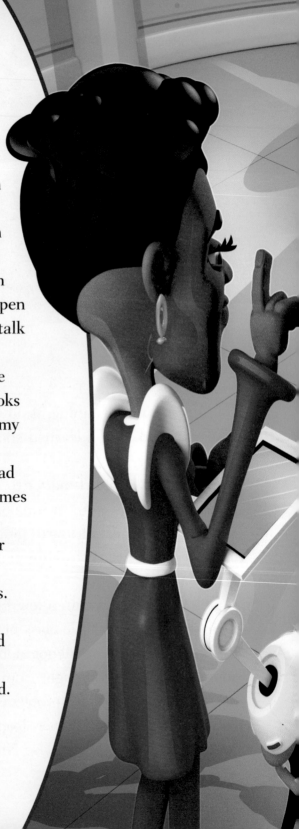

chapter 2

The Field Trip

As moon day turned to moon night, we could tell that Johnny and Carmen had a lot in common. Johnny sat next to Carmen every day and chatted with her about rocks as though he'd been collecting them his whole life. Carmen was somewhat shy, but she began to open up. Eventually she and Johnny would talk for hours after class.

Meanwhile I was overjoyed to have someone with whom I could share books and ideas. Ned had read nearly all of my favorite books, and he was perfectly willing to read some of the poems I had written. He taught me various new games he enjoyed. Before long I was beating him at Mars Conquest at least once or twice a week.

When moon day arrived again, Ms. Anderson told us about our next field trip. We would take the moon bus and visit the place where the first humans had landed on the moon. I was excited. I love moon history.

As usual, Johnny had to tell us all about the first moon landing by the crew of *Apollo 11*. He was like a book with too many pages: each time you opened him up, a bunch of facts fell out. He reminded us that Neil Armstrong was the first human to set foot on the moon, followed immediately by Buzz Aldrin. He said that Armstrong got all the credit just because he was first! Between the two of them, they carried back 46 pounds of lunar rocks for the scientists on Earth.

Ms. Anderson informed us of all the school's rules about how to behave on the field trip. We had to wear our heavy space **attire**. We had to check the suits first to **ensure** that they were in working order. We had to stay seated on the bus as long as it was in motion. When we got out of the bus, we had to hold hands (or clasp gloves) and stay together.

Carmen, Jackie, Ajani, and I were quite familiar with these rules; we'd heard them many times. They were new to Ned and Johnny, though, and I'm afraid Ned felt a bit let down.

"I thought we'd have a chance to explore!" he said.

"You can explore the surface a little," said Ms. Anderson, "but we prefer to keep you all together. We want to be sure nobody bounces too far off."

She continued, "You see, the moon's gravity is so weak that you can jump six times farther or higher than you could on Earth. You students might get overly excited and attempt a high jump or a long jump. In no time at all, you could find that you'd leaped far away from the rest of us. I truly don't want anyone to get lost. The bus must leave on time to get us all back safely with our air supply intact. These rules are designed for your safety."

Johnny, of course, had to tell us all exactly how powerful lunar gravity was and exactly how different it was from the gravity on Earth. With a quick sketch on the board, he compared lunar gravity to gravity on Jupiter, Venus, and Mars. Ms. Anderson was always surprised at how much he knew, but I now knew he was extremely smart! He wasn't a bad teacher, either. With his help, math problems were starting to make sense to me.

After school we walked together to the dressing rooms at the port, where we all tested our space suits. I pulled on my heavy helmet and fastened my uncomfortable boots and gloves. As much as I enjoyed exploring, I was always grateful when we came back from a field trip and could take off our awful suits. Ajani didn't even fit into his suit anymore. He had to visit the lab to get fitted for a new one.

At last the day arrived, and we were ready to go. Chattering and giggling, we put on our space suits and filed into the port, where we took our places on the moon bus. Naturally Johnny sat next to Carmen, and I took a seat next to Ned. The driver checked our suits and air supplies, and then with a whoosh we took off.

The moon bus traveled quickly just above the surface of the moon. It skimmed the surface like pictures I'd seen of an insect flying low over a pond. Ned enjoyed every moment of the trip. He watched out the window and pointed out landmarks—a rock that looked a little like a crabby man's face, a crater in the shape of a lake back on Earth. I had seen them all before, but they seemed new when he showed them to me.

Jackie was the first one to see the flag, the very flag that had been planted by Armstrong and Aldrin so many decades ago.

"We're here!" she cried. We all crowded around to look out the window. The flag stood alone on a white expanse of moon dust, surrounded by silent, curved moon hills that reminded me of sand dunes along the ocean.

Johnny began at once to relate some key facts about the American flag. "Hey," said Jackie in a joking tone, "I'm actually from the United States. It's my flag. I know all about it!"

I'm originally from Namibia, so I was not really aware of the history of the American flag. The Namibian flag has a blue stripe, a red stripe, and a green stripe. It also has a sun. These represent different things, such as our people, peace, and our natural resources. I wasn't entirely sure what the stars on the American flag meant.

"You can tell me all about it," I told Johnny.

The field trip started out well. We left the ship hand-in-hand and picked our way carefully around stones and boulders. Each footstep seemed light and easy, and we covered the ground very quickly.

"You may explore as far as that hill," Ms. Anderson said, pointing to a small rise 500 meters away. "Stay together, and please don't venture past that point. Remember the rules we discussed earlier." She watched us from the bus as we set out across the chalky surface.

The six of us, still linked together, strolled in the direction of the hill. At one point Carmen stopped to observe some small, sparkly rocks. Her space suit glove wasn't designed for fine movement, so she couldn't pick them up.

"I will get them for you, Carmen," said Johnny. In a flash he took off his glove, picked up the rocks, and put his glove back on.

I was too surprised to speak. Ajani was extremely upset. "Don't do that, Johnny!" he cried. "You'll burn your skin!" Before we'd left on the bus, Jackie had informed us that the temperature outside was just above that of boiling water. Imagine sticking

your hand into a pot of bubbling soup. That's what our crazy pal Johnny had just done, yet he seemed to feel no ill effects.

We all stared at Johnny in amazement. He shrugged and looked unconcerned. "Carmen wanted the rocks," he explained in his tinny voice.

In no time at all, we'd reached the hill. As we started to walk back, Ned unexpectedly dropped my hand.

"I just want to see how it feels," he declared. He began to skip. Each time he landed, his next jump took him even higher and farther than before.

"Be super careful," I chuckled. "Don't forget what Ms. Anderson said."

The others had nearly arrived back at the bus, and Ms. Anderson was just starting to count her students. Only Johnny turned back to look at us. As he did, Ned's last skip took him over the hill—and out of sight.

What happened next is almost too strange
to describe. Ms. Anderson started to sprint after Ned,
but her space suit was just too big and clunky for rapid
movement. She nearly fell as her boots caught on
a rock.

Suddenly we all heard a shout as Johnny flashed
past Ms. Anderson. Ajani stood near me, shouting
wildly. For reasons I couldn't entirely understand, he
held Johnny's empty space suit in his arms.

We all stood still, staring. Johnny moved across the
surface of the moon just as if he were on roller skates.
In a single moment he was past the hill. We all
held our breath, wondering what could
possibly happen next. In another
moment, Johnny returned, toting
Ned on his back.

Now Johnny was definitely not a large boy. In fact, if we stood back to back, I'm sure he'd be shorter than I am. However, he held Ned on his back as easily as I would carry a teddy bear, and he did it all without wearing a space suit. The intense white light told me that the surface of the moon was boiling. I knew without any doubt in my mind that the lunar atmosphere wasn't possible for humans to breathe.

Johnny set Ned down gently, took his space suit from Ajani, and climbed onto the bus. One by one, we all climbed in after him, none of us willing or able to say a word about what we'd just seen. Carmen sat down beside Johnny, her eyes wide, questioning, and perhaps a little bit fearful.

"Here are those rocks you wanted," he told her. We all just stared.

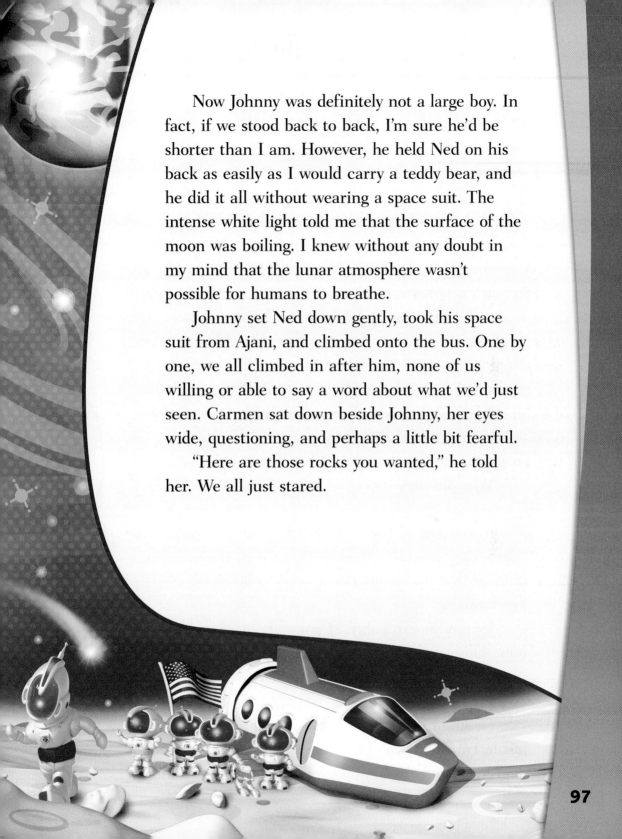

chapter 3
The Truth about Johnny

Ned was in class the next Earth day, apparently none the worse for his lunar adventure—but Johnny was nowhere to be seen. After we settled in at our desks, Ms. Anderson told us the truth about Johnny. We were silent as she spoke.

"I am sure you've all figured out by now that Johnny was not exactly human," she began. "He was part of an important Earth experiment. Scientists on Earth created robots to work with us humans on the moon. The robots were designed to do some jobs that we cannot do. For example, as we dig for water deeper below the moon's surface, the work has new dangers. Robots can handle those dangers better than we can. They are designed to stand great heat and great cold, and of course, they don't need to breathe air, eat food, or sleep."

"Why did they make the robots look human?" Carmen asked.

"It was part of the experiment," said Ms. Anderson. "Since they would live and work with us, the scientists thought that the robots should look and behave like humans."

"Johnny was so polite," I pointed out. "He didn't seem quite human. Compare him to Ajani, for example!"

"Hey!" complained Ajani. I smiled sweetly at him, and even Carmen giggled.

"He knew so much about everything!" said Jackie. "I mean, I'm smart, you know, but Johnny was smart to a **degree** beyond any kid I'd ever met. He knew so much!"

"The scientists put all that into his computer system," explained Ms. Anderson. "They provided him with plenty of facts, and then they added a **program** that told him how to behave."

"He certainly had me fooled," admitted Ned. "I spent a lot of time with him before we left for the moon, and I never dreamed that he was something other than human."

"Why can't Johnny stay with us?" asked Ajani. "I was starting to like the guy."

"You're right," I agreed. "Johnny was turning into part of our team. I can't believe that we have to go to class without him, whether he's a robot or not." I was especially worried about my math scores. I didn't want to think how I'd pass the next math test without Johnny's great teaching help.

"Well," said Ms. Anderson, shaking her head, "the experiment did not work exactly the way the scientists hoped. Johnny was supposed to behave like a human, but he did more than the scientists expected. He was supposed to assist us. He was also supposed to obey rules, just like we all do."

"He saved me!" cried Ned.

"That may be true," said Ms. Anderson, "but he did it in a way that put you all in danger. What if you'd taken off your glove or your space suit, just because Johnny did?"

"We know better!" I said. "We'd never do anything so foolish." Honestly, sometimes people treat us like such **infants**. Just because Ned acted silly and went skipping over the hill didn't make me want to do the same thing. We're not all that childish. I consider myself very levelheaded. I'd never do anything dangerous just because I saw someone else doing it.

"Well, students," said Ms. Anderson, "the whole adventure just shows that there are some things the scientists had not considered when they programmed Johnny. Now they'll probably go back and try designing a different kind of robot. We'll need to wait for a while to see what they create."

We all thought that was a terrible idea. We liked Johnny. Yes, he was a robot, but he was also our friend.

"Ms. Anderson," said Jackie, "please don't let them send Johnny back to Earth. We can keep him here while they try out different ideas."

After a certain amount of begging and pleading, we got Ms. Anderson to see what a good plan this was. In the end we had to write long, pleading letters and talk to some very important people, but we saved Johnny. The Earth scientists agreed to let him stay on the moon, and he is part of our class once again. Our little robot pal is not allowed to go on field trips, but he comes to class and assists me with my math problems. He sits next to Carmen and talks to her about rocks. He's always very polite, especially to Ms. Anderson, and he knows everything about everything. He also obeys all the rules.

Things are going very well here on Moon Base Nine. The boredom of moon life is gone, and our little class has fun every day. We are all different individuals—some of us are not even human—but we all honestly like and help each other. That's what really matters.

Focus Question: How might space be a part of our future?

A Check Understanding ★

Using ideas from the selection, make a list of the ways space may be a part of our future. Do you think these events will happen? PRACTICE COMPANION 359

B Understand Literary Elements ★★

A motive is the reason why a character does something. Motives tell you what a character wants. What are Jamila's motives in the story? What do these tell you about her character? Discuss your answers with a partner.

C Share and Compare ★★

With a partner, compare your list of the ways space may be a part of our future. How does your partner's list differ from yours? How is it the same?

D Think Critically ★★★★

Why do people study space? Use examples from the selection to explain.

My Home Page

Respond to the THEME Question

Why do people study space?

Use these activities to show what you've learned about the theme question.

Design and Create

1. Imagine that you discovered a new constellation. Design your own model of it.

2. Draw your constellation on black construction paper. Cut out small holes for stars to form the shape of the constellation.

3. Shine a light behind the paper to see the shape that the stars would make in the sky.

Multimedia

1. With a partner, design two Web pages about space and space exploration. Include the text and pictures that you want on your Web pages.

2. Present your Web page designs to the class.

Book Club

1. Choose your favorite selection from the unit. Tell your group why you chose it.

2. Read your favorite part aloud.

3. Search for other books about space to read and share.

Be an Author

1. Imagine that your town is located on the moon.

2. Write a story that describes your daily life. Think about how life on the moon is different from the life you live on Earth. Be sure to include dialogue between characters.

3. Read your story to a friend.

Glossary

analyze (an′ ə līz′) *v.* to study something carefully; to find out what something is made of;
Carla likes to analyze rock samples. **72**

assist (ə sist′) *v.* to support or help;
The hospital worker is there to assist people who need help. **87**

assume (ə sōōm′) *v.* to think something is true;
May we assume that you will arrive on time? **50**

astrologer (ə strol′ ə jər) *n.* a person who studies the influence that stars and planets are supposed to have on people and events;
An astrologer studied the sky and told me to expect good luck. **7**

attire (ə tīr′) *n.* clothing;
Winter attire is often mittens, wool hats, scarves, and heavy coats. **89**

bashful (bash′ fəl) *adj.* shy;
Kyo was bashful when he first came to our class but now he's friends with everyone. **85**

clergy (klûr′ jē) *n.* a person who is officially appointed to do religious work;
Rabbis, priests, ministers, and imams are some members of the clergy. **9**

collapse (kə laps′) *v.* to fall in; to close up; to lose strength;
That stack of blocks will collapse if you pull out the bottom block. **42**

comprehend (kom′ pri hend′) *v.* to understand;
Can you comprehend this article about pollen and allergies? **37**

degree (di grē′) *n.* a measure or level;
Eduardo played his position with a greater degree of skill than he has had before. **98**

distribute (di strib′ yōōt) *v.* to give out;
The vegetable market will distribute its sale flyers throughout the neighborhood. **21**

ensure (en shōōr′) *v.* to make certain;
When you use a seat belt, you help to ensure your safety in the car. **89**

flung (flung) *v.* past tense and past participle of *fling*: to throw forcefully;
Aaron would have flung his baseball hat onto the rack across the room if he could. **13**

formation (fôr mā′ shən) *n.* something that is made, arranged, or formed, as in a pattern;
The cheerleaders made a pyramid formation by standing on each other's shoulders. **70**

gaze (gāz) *v.* to look at something for a long time; I could gaze at that painting for hours. **43**

genius (jēn′ yəs) *n.* a person who has a great ability to do something or who is very capable intellectually;
Arianne is a genius when it comes to creating interesting recipes. **57**

gravity (gra′ vi tē) *n.* the force that pulls things toward Earth;
Gravity is the force that pulls items down when you toss them into the air. **26**

hilarious (hi lair′ ē əs) *adj.* extremely funny;
Grandpa Bernie tells some hilarious stories, and we all laugh for hours. **61**

illustrate (il′ ə strāt′) *v.* to make clear or explain, especially by drawing; I asked Martina to illustrate my story. **83**

immense (i mens′) *adj.* extremely big; The explorer saw an immense elephant blocking the path ahead. **40**

infant (in′ fənt) *n.* a baby; The infant slept quietly in his crib. **101**

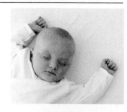

lunar (lōō′ nər) *adj.* having to do with the moon; The lunar surface is covered with light and shadow. **37**

magnificent (mag ni′ fə sənt) *adj.* very grand and beautiful; We were a magnificent sight in our costumes for the play. **62**

marvel (mär′ vəl) *v.* to feel a sense of wonder or astonishment; I always marvel at the beautiful colors of tropical birds. **76**

menacingly (men′ is ing lē) *adv.* as if to threaten; The dog snarled menacingly, but in truth he was just frightened. **74**

minor (mī′ nər) *adj.* not very important; Brad made a minor change in the title of this paper. **64**

navigate (nav′ i gāt′) *v.* to sail or steer a course on or through something; Airplane pilots have dashboard gauges that help them navigate safely. **34**

nudge (nuj) *v.* to touch or push gently; My sister will nudge Dad to wake him up. **62**

observatory (əb zûr′ və tôr′ ē) *n.* a building with equipment that is used to look at the stars, planets, and other things in space; Our class visited the observatory and saw the giant telescope. **35**

passion (pash′ ən) *n.* a strong desire or liking for something; Uncle Joe has a passion for baseball and will watch any game any time. **15**

permission (pər mish′ ən) *n.*
approval or consent;
I have my parents' permission to go to
Ashley's sleepover party. **69**

perplex (pər pleks′) *v.* to puzzle;
Algebra continues to perplex me, but I
will continue to try to learn it. **13**

program (prō′ gram′) *n.* a series of
coded instructions, as for a computer;
This new
program makes
my computer run
much faster. **99**

pursue (pər sōō′) *v.* to follow; to
continue with something;
Tamara would like to pursue a career
in animation. **16**

reflect (ri flekt′) *v.* to give back; to
bounce off;
A sheet of aluminum foil will reflect
heat. **24**

regret (ri gret′) *v.* to feel very sorry
about;
I regret leaving my papers on the floor
where the puppy could chew them. **74**

revolve (ri volv′) *v.* to move in a
circle around a center point;
The bees revolve around the flowers in
the middle of the garden. **11**

rotate (rō′ tāt) *v.* to turn on an axis;
A car's wheels rotate on the axles. **11**

sibling (sib′ ling)
n. a brother or a
sister;
My sister is my
only sibling. **9**

speck (spek) *n.* a small spot;
There is a little speck of ketchup on
Dad's tie. **30**

telescope (te′ lə skōp′)
n. an instrument that
makes faraway objects
seem larger and closer;
We used a small telescope
to scan the horizon for
ships. **24**

Index

A

Andromeda Galaxy, 50–51
Aristarchus, 14, 15, 18
astrolabe, 17, 36
astronomy, 10, 30
    tools to study, 35–39

B

Bruno, Giordano, 23

C

Centaurus (constellation), 32
Copernicus, Nicolaus, 6–27, 37
    books by, 20–22, 24
    childhood of, 7–9
    education of, 8, 10–15
    ideas about astronomy, 16–24
    influence of, 23–24, 26, 27
    tools used by, 16, 17
cross-staff, 38

G

galaxies, 48, 49, 50
Galileo Galilei, 24, 37
Gemini (constellation), 32
geocentric theory, 11–13, 15
Glenn, John, 27

H

heliocentric theory, 14, 20, 21, 23, 24, 26, 27
Hubble Telescope, 43

L

light years and speed of light, 40–41, 43

M

Mars, 13, 17, 18
Milky Way, 48, 49

N

nebula, 42
Newton, Isaac, 26
nuclear fusion, 42

O

Orion (constellation), 31
Osiander, 22

P

planets
    geocentric theory and, 12
    heliocentric theory and, 14
    orbits around sun, 25
Polaris, the North Star, 34
Ptolemy, 11–12, 13, 24

Q

quadrant, 38

R

red dwarfs, 44, 45
red supergiants, 44, 45
Rheticus, George, 21–22
Roemer, Olaus, 41

S

seasons, star patterns and, 33
sextant, 39
sky charts, 52–53
solar systems, 48, 50
space, studying, 4–27
stars, 30–53
    constellations of, 30, 31–32
    life of, studying, 42–43
    as map, 34
    poems, songs, and stories about,
        46–47
    seasons and patterns of, 33
    types of, 44–45, 48
Stonehenge, 34
sun, gravity of, 26

T

telescopes, 24, 37, 43, 72

U

universe, 48, 50–51, 52

W

Watzenrode, Lucas, 9
white dwarfs, 44, 45

Acknowledgments

Photo Credits: Cover ©Ralph Morse/Time Life Pictures/Getty Images; **4** ©Hulton Archive/Getty Images; **5** (tl) ©Alamy Images, (tr) ©Leda_d/Shutterstock, (bl) ©Comstock Images/Alamy, (br) ©NASA; **6** ©William Radcliffe/Science Faction/Corbis; **6–27** (border thru-out) ©Pixtal/AGE Fotostock; **8** ©Pixtal/AGE Fotostock; **10** ©Pegaz/Alamy; **11** ©Joos van Gent/The Bridgeman Art Library/Getty Images; **13** ©Andrea Pistolesi/The Image Bank/Getty Images; **15** ©Interfoto Pressebildagentur/Alamy; **16** ©Sherab/Alamy; **17** (l) ©Jupiter Images/Ablestock/Alamy, (tr) ©Bettmann/Corbis; **18** ©Archive Timothy McCarthy/Art Resource, NY; **20** ©The Print Collector/Alamy; **21** ©The London Art Archive/Alamy; **22** ©Bettmann/Corbis; **23** ©Interfoto Pressebildagentur/Alamy; **24** ©The Granger Collection, New York; **25** (Mercury) ©Alamy Images, (Venus) ©Alamy Images, (Earth) ©Alamy Images, (Jupiter) ©NASA, (Saturn) ©GettyImages, (Uranus) ©NASA, (Neptune) ©GettyImages, (Mars) ©Getty Images; **26** ©The Granger Collection, New York; **27** ©Ralph Morse/Time Life Pictures/Getty Images; **28** ©Pixtal/AGE Fotostock; **29** (l) ©Leda_d/Shutterstock, (r) ©Alamy Images; **33** ©The Granger Collection, New York; **34** ©tharrison/Istock; **35** ©Phillip Kramer/Getty Images; **36** ©Coston Stock/Alamy; **37** ©Hulton Archive/Getty Images; **38** (t) ©Bettmann/Corbis, (b) ©North Wind Picture Archives/Alamy; **39** (t) ©Walter Hensaw/Peter Ifland Collection, (b) ©Friedrich Saurer/Alamy; **40–41** ©Brand X Pictures/Punchstock; **41** ©Jerry Lodriguss/Photo Researchers, Inc.; **42** ©StockTrek/SuperStock; **43** ©Wayne Levin/The Image Bank/Getty Images; **45** (bkgrd) ©STSc1/NASA/Corbis, (t) ©StockTrek/SuperStock, (b) ©Science Photo Library/Alamy; **46–47** ©Robert Postma/Getty Images; **48–49** ©Digital Stock/Corbis; **50–51** ©Robert Gendler/Visuals Unlimited, Inc./Getty Images; **52–53** ©Jan Tyler/IStockphoto/Getty Images; **54** ©Digital Stock/Corbis; **55** (t) ©NASA, (b) ©Comstock Images/Alamy;.**79** (t) ©Brand X Pictures/PunchStock, (b) ©Pixtal/Agefotostock.

Art Credits: 9, 17 ©The McGraw-Hill Companies, Inc./Jeff Mangiat; **12, 14** ©The McGraw-Hill Companies, Inc./Robert Schuster; **19** ©The McGraw-Hill Companies, Inc./Robert Schuster; **30–31, 32–33** ©The McGraw-Hill Companies, Inc./John Schreiner; **56–78** ©The McGraw-Hill Companies, Inc./Rosemary & Mark Jarman; **80–103** ©The McGraw-Hill Companies, Inc./Pixelboy Studios.